THE BLUES BROTHERS

GW00580227

SHE CAUGHT THE KATY

PETER GUNN THEME   3

GIMME SOME LOVIN'   12

SHAKE A TAILFEATHER   15

EVERYBODY NEEDS SOMEBODY TO LOVE   20

THE OLD LANDMARK   30

THINK   26

THEME FROM RAWHIDE   36

MINNIE THE MOOCHER   42

SWEET HOME CHICAGO   48

JAILHOUSE ROCK   54

© International Music Publications Ltd
First published in 1994 by International Music Publications Ltd
revised edition published in 1997
International Music Publications Ltd is a Faber Music company
3 Queen Square, London WC1N 3AU
Production: Stephen Clark and Sadie Cook
Printed in England by Caligraving Ltd
All rights reserved

ISBN 0-571-52578-4

To buy Faber Music publications or to find out about the full range of titles available,
please contact your local music retailer or Faber Music sales enquiries:

Faber Music Ltd, Burnt Mill, Elizabeth Way, Harlow, CM20 2HX England
Tel: +44(0)1279 82 89 82   Fax: +44(0)1279 82 89 83
sales@fabermusic.com   fabermusic.com

PETER GUNN THEME

By HENRY MANCINI

SHE CAUGHT THE KATY

Words and Music by
TAJ MAHAL and YANK RACHEL

repeat to fade

GIMME SOME LOVIN'

Words and Music by STEVE WINWOOD,
MUFF WINWOOD and SPENCER DAVIS

Well, my tem - pera - ture's ris - ing and my feet left the floor,___
Well, my head's___ ex - plod - ing and I'm float - ing to sound,

Well, I feel so good everything is getting hot,
You'd better take some time off 'cos the place is on fire.
Better start baby, 'cos I have so much to do,
We made it baby, and it happened to you,
And I'm so glad we made it.
I want you, gimme some alovin', gimme some alovin',
Gimme some alovin', every day.

SHAKE A TAILFEATHER

Words and Music by
O HAYES, WILLIAMS and RICE

EVERYBODY NEEDS SOMEBODY TO LOVE

Words and Music by BERT BERNS,
SOLOMON BURKE and JERRY WEXLER

you.

THINK

Words and Music by
TED WHITE and ARETHA FRANKLIN

let your-self be free. Peo-ple walk-in' round ev - 'ry day, play-in' games and talk-ing scores. Tryin'

— to make oth - er peo - ple lose their minds. Well, be care - ful you don't lose yours. Oh.

D.$ al Coda

CODA

You need me__ and I need you.__ We out each oth - er, there ain't no-

- thin' eith - er can do. Oh,_____ hey, think a-bout me. (To the bone for deepness)

repeat to fade

THE OLD LANDMARK

Words and Music by
ADELINE BRUNNER

THEME FROM RAWHIDE

Words by NED WASHINGTON
Music by DIMITRI TIOMKIN

Roll - in' roll - in' roll - in'   roll - in' roll - in' roll - in'   roll - in' roll - in' roll - in'

roll - in' roll - in' roll - in' raw - hide.

Roll - in' roll - in' roll - in'   though the streams are swoll - en,

MINNIE, THE MOOCHER

Words and Music by
CAB CALLOWAY and IRVING MILLS

SWEET HOME CHICAGO

Words and Music by
HERMAN PARKER

same old___ place,   sweet home_____ Chi - ca - go.___

Well_____ one and one is two,   six and two is eight,___
Six and three is nine,   nine and nine is eight-teen,

come on_____ ba - by don't you   make me late. Hi - de - hey,
look there bro - ther ba - by and a   see what I   see.___ Hi - de - hey,

ba - by don't you wan - na go,_____   back_ to that

JAILHOUSE ROCK

Words and Music by
JERROR LEIBER and MIKE STOLLER

4. The sad sack was a-sittin' on a block of stone,
   Way over in the corner weeping all alone.
   The warden said, 'Hey buddy, don't you be no square,
   If you can't find a partner, use a wooden chair!'
   Let's rock, etc.

5. Shiftly Henry said to Bugs, 'For Heaven's sake,
   No one's lookin', now's our chance to make a break.'
   Bugsy turned to Shifty and he said, 'Nix, nix,
   I wanna stick around a while and get my kicks.'
   Let's rock, etc.